Piano Exam Pieces

ABRSM Grade 2

Selected from the 2013 & 2014 syllabus

Name

Date of exam

Contents

Editor for ABRSM: Richard Jones

† This arrangement only

First published in 2012 by ABRSM (Publishing) Ltd, a wholly owned subsidiary of ABRSM, 24 Portland Place, London W1B 1LU, United Kingdom © 2012 by The Associated Board of the Royal Schools of Music

Music origination by Julia Bovee Cover by Kate Benjamin & Andy Potts Printed in England by Halstan & Co. Ltd, Amersham, Bucks.

MIX
Paper from responsible sources
FSC™ C109619

A:1

Hornpipe

from *Abdelazer*, Z. T683

Henry Purcell
(1659–95)

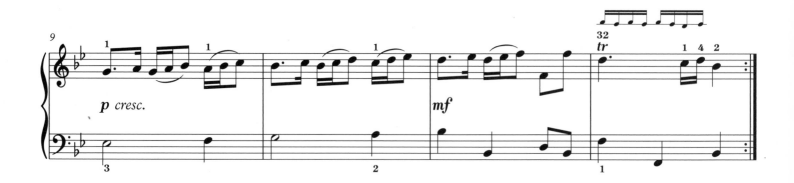

English music of the Restoration period is dominated by the figure of Henry Purcell, one of the greatest composers the country has ever produced. He wrote incidental music and songs for over 40 plays, one of which is *Abdelazer, or The Moor's Revenge* by Aphra Behn. The hornpipe selected here is a keyboard transcription of a hornpipe for strings from Purcell's incidental music for *Abdelazer*. The hornpipe was, at that time, a popular British dance, related to the jig and to certain types of country dance.

The first repeat should be played in the exam. All slurs and dynamics are editorial suggestions only. In the source, trills are given in the form of two sloping strokes: ⁄.

Source: London, British Library, Add. MS 22099

Adapted from *Baroque Keyboard Pieces*, Book I, edited by Richard Jones (ABRSM)

Très vite

Third movement from Fantaisie in E minor, TWV 33:21

A:2

G. P. Telemann
(1681–1767)

Très vite [♩ = c.92]

Très vite Very quick

Georg Philipp Telemann published three sets of *Fantaisies pour le clavessin* (Fantasies for the Harpsichord), each containing a dozen pieces. Like J. S. Bach's *Italian Concerto* and *French Overture*, written around the same time, these pieces were designed to illustrate the differences between the fashionable French and Italian styles of the day. The 'second dozen', from which this piece is selected, is written in the French style, whereas the first and third dozen are Italian.

This piece has an indeterminate dance rhythm, rather like the *bourrée*. Unslurred crotchets might be lightly detached. All slurs and dynamics are editorial suggestions only. Players with small hands could omit the bottom E in the last chord.

Source: *Fantaisies pour le clavessin*, TWV 33 (Hamburg, 1732/3)

Adapted from Telemann: *Fantaisies, Second Dozen*, edited by Richard Jones (ABRSM)

Allegro

First movement from Sonatina No. 2 in C

Thomas Attwood
(1765–1838)

The English organist and composer Thomas Attwood enjoyed royal patronage throughout his life. In his early years he studied in Naples and then in Vienna, where he received composition lessons from Mozart, who said of him: 'He partakes more of my style than any scholar I ever had; and I predict that he will prove a sound musician.'

This piece is selected from Attwood's *Easy Progressive Lessons* – a set of four sonatinas for keyboard students. All dynamics and slurs are editorial suggestions only.

Source: *Easy Progressive Lessons Fingered for Young Beginners on the Piano Forte or Harpsichord* (London, *c.*1795)

Adapted from Attwood: *Easy Progressive Lessons*, edited by Richard Jones (ABRSM)

Bear Dance

from *Nicolai Podgornov's Graded Pieces for Piano*, Vol. 1

Nicolai Podgornov
(born 1950)

B:1

Nicolai Podgornov was born in Leningrad (now St Petersburg), but since 1991 has lived and worked in Germany. He has much experience of performing rock, jazz and pop music, as well as composing for the cinema, theatre and television.

A suitably 'bearish' performance of this dance would sound rather ungainly and ponderous, but with an unmistakable touch of the comic.

[B:2]

Lullaby

No. 5 from *Six Sketches*

C. V. Stanford
(1852–1924)

The Irish-born composer Charles Stanford studied at Cambridge University, where he was an organ scholar at Queens' College, and then the organist of Trinity College. He became professor of music of the university in 1887. Earlier, in 1883, he had been appointed professor of composition at the Royal College of Music, and remarkably he managed to keep both positions going at the same time. He was not only a highly prolific composer but a very influential teacher, whose pupils included Vaughan Williams, Holst, Ireland and Howells.

Stanford's *Six Sketches* for piano, from which this piece is selected, date from 1918. A way to approach this charming lullaby would be to bring out its slow lilt, which is no doubt intended to imitate the rocking of the cradle. All slurs are original, except those in the left hand of bb. 17–18, which are editorial suggestions only. The ties in the left hand of bb. 17–18 are also editorial.

Source: *Six Sketches for Pianoforte* (London: Joseph Williams, 1918)

AB 3629

Xiong mao

No. 1 from *Dong Wu Yuan zu qu*

B:3

Li Yinghai
(1927–2007)

Xiong mao The Panda; **Dong Wu Yuan zu qu** The Zoo Suite

Li Yinghai composed his suite *The Zoo*, from which this piece is taken, in 1985. It is included in *Selection from Chinese Classical Music for Piano*, Book 4 (Shi Dai Wen Yi Publishing House, China).

    The title refers to the giant panda, with its black and white fur and black eye patches, which is native to north-west China and Tibet. The quiet, gentle tone of the piece suggests that the panda is engaged in its main activity – feeding on bamboo shoots, which it does about 12 hours per day.

Meet the Flintstones

William Hanna (1910–2001), Joseph Barbera
(1911–2006) and Hoyt Curtin (1922–2000)

Arranged by Nicholas Scott-Burt

The Flintstones is a cartoon situation comedy about a Stone Age family that originally ran on American television from 1960 to 1966. It was created and directed by William Hanna and Joseph Barbera. The theme music was by the American composer and arranger Hoyt Curtin, who also wrote the music for other Hanna-Barbera cartoons, such as *Scooby-Doo* and *Top Cat*.

In this piano arrangement, it is equally acceptable in the exam to play the last right-hand chord down an octave.

Polka

from *Leichte Tänze*, Book 2

C:2

Mátyás Seiber
(1905–60)

Leichte Tänze Easy Dances

The Hungarian composer Mátyás Seiber studied with Kodály at the Budapest Academy (1919–24), but in 1935 he settled in England, where he became a lecturer at Morley College, London (1942–57) and established a fine reputation as a teacher of composition.

The *polka* is a Bohemian dance for couples in a moderately fast 2/4 time. It became very popular throughout Europe and America in the 19th century.

The paired semiquavers in bb. 12–13 are unmarked, so it might be effective to slur them as a contrast to the prevailing staccato. All dynamics are editorial suggestions only.

© 1937 SCHOTT MUSIC, Mainz – Germany
Reproduced by permission. All rights reserved. All enquiries about this piece, apart from those directly relating to the exams, should be addressed to Schott Music Ltd, 48 Great Marlborough Street, London W1F 7BB.

C:3

Strange Things Happen

Sarah Watts

Sarah Watts was a student at the Royal College of Music, where she studied bassoon and piano. She was inspired at an early age by her mother who played jazz at home, and who encouraged her to improvise. Nowadays one of her main musical activities is composition. As well as writing piano music, she has published musicals, choral works, and several books of educational music for woodwind instruments, including the *Red Hot Recorder* and *Razzamajazz* series.

Strange Things Happen is written in the style of 1930s swing. For a stylistic performance, try to imagine the left hand as a pizzicato double bass, keeping a solid rhythm throughout.

01/13